# Spot's Fun-time

## Colouring Book

## Eric Hill

Yummy! Spot enjoys a bowl
of porridge in the morning.

"Good morning birds!"
says Spot.

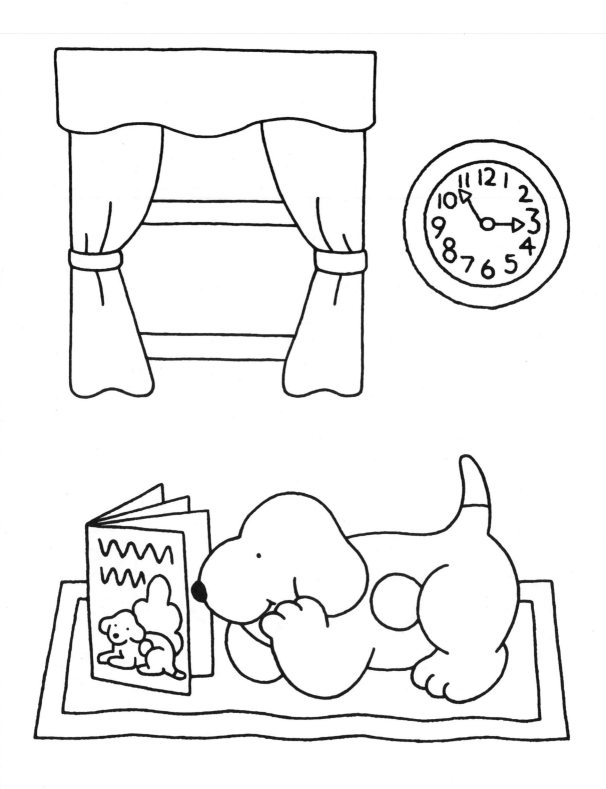

Spot loves to read books.

Spot loves riding
on his toy horse.

Spot likes drawing pictures.

Spot can write his name.
Can you?

"Hello," says Spot.

Spot loves his friends,
Helen and Tom.

Helen dresses up
as a fairy princess.

Spot dresses up
as a wizard.

Yippee!
Now Spot is a cowboy.

Bang! Bang! Spot and Helen
make lots of noise on their drums.

Tom plays a tune
on his guitar.

Now Spot is the band leader.

Spot loves his mum and dad and
his grandma and grandpa too.

Spot and Grandma share
a story in the garden.

Spot helps out with the dusting.
"Well done, Spot," says Grandma.

Spot finds a rabbit
eating Grandpa's carrots.

Spot and Helen love
dressing up for Grandma.

Spot and his friends
are in a show!

It's a lovely sunny day.
Spot is going out to play.

Spot loves to run and jump.

"It's fun to fly my kite,"
says Spot.